WORDS
UNBURDEN ME

by Ninth-Grade English Language Learners from
South High School with 826 MSP

D1547727

826
MSP

ISBN 13: 978-1-63489-438-8

Library of Congress Catalog Number has been applied for.
Printed in the United States of America
First Printing: 2021

25 24 23 22 21   5 4 3 2 1

Cover design by Kprecia Ambers
Interior design by Patrick Maloney

Wise Ink Creative Publishing
807 Broadway St NE
Suite 46
Minneapolis, MN, 55413

"I reflect on their struggle, their determination, and the strength of their vision—to see what can be, unburdened by what has been. And I stand on their shoulders."

—**Kamala Harris,**
Nov. 7, 2020

CONTENTS

OUR LIVES

APPENDIX

FOREWORD

By Maria Isa

We are survivors reclaiming our strength, honoring our ancestors, and rising to our goals.

Finding ways to connect and recognizing actions of survival is a strength. Una fuerza to learn and reflect on the journeys of our ancestors and the legacies of their strength that were born within each of us to achieve and empower. Along with strength comes the reminder of the traumas we carry from generations before us. Trauma brought upon history and political control of racism and discrimination toward indigenous communities and communities of color; targeting our youth to cut their connection with being able to dream, set goals, and aspire. Those traumas can come from surviving migration, insecurities, racism, sexism, and physical, mental, and drug abuse—the many illnesses that come with trying to manage overcoming disadvantages and not being born into white privilege.

I entered the Writers' Room at Minneapolis South High School this year and embraced the energy of blossoming minds polishing creativity and recognizing the power of writing as medicine. The diverse classroom of beautiful minds, yearning to connect, made me revisit how it's important to take time to share. To take time to listen. To take time to break bread. To take time to learn something new about each other along with making time to complement and set goals. The youth I was able to engage with come from all over the world. They have different traditions, religions, diets, languages, styles.

High schoolers are given the option of two things in this system: pass and rise or fail and get out. We're forced in this system to "follow the line, check the box, sign here," barricaded from being able to express, share, and be true to our own selves, our experiences, and our journeys—not only in society but even in our own homes. Working with the youth in this program, I wanted to express that it's okay to feel scared, tired, worried, let down, upset, and angry, but what isn't okay is to lose sight of yourself, to not thrive, and to not love yourself. In our world, many of our environments want us to thrive for the best, yet the places that provide the most support, like our schools, can still break us due to the traumatic structures our society continues to uphold. "YOU KNOW, LIKE THE HATERS," I recall a student in my second hour shouted out when we outlined ten individual goals each student wrote down. Before discussing goals and our personal challenges and skills to overcome and achieve, we circled as a village and looked at the world map to see how far each of us had come from our ancestral villages to the village we were now in as a classroom in South Minneapolis. I recall one of my students asking, "What if I'm Native? And my village has always been here?" I then responded, "You are a true warrior of this land, who leads the rhythm of connecting our ancestors' legacies to survive together and connect like the water does to land in this world."

Our differences and similarities are what give us strength and help us recognize that by unifying and building our dreams, we can keep as focused as possible amongst the trials and turbulence we face through the traumas we have survived. Those challenges are what we must face and overcome to achieve the goals we set and we decide as individuals.

As I reflect on my short time with the program, I am sad, because I miss each of those students. I miss their smiles, their jokes, and their personalities. Their creativity and responses. I miss how we were connecting as a class who recognized our importance in making history. This pandemic we are all living in makes me—like many of our students—worried, scared, bored, and stressed as to what is to come from the unknown. I put my thoughts into good energy and faith within each and every one of them. I hope that their opportunities learned and achieved in this program and our time becoming a village together while in that Writers' Room allow them to write each and every emotion and action into their journeys, to achieve and to recognize how much they have survived in this world already, to prepare them as best as possible to be the young warriors that they are today. To the history makers in this book, each and every one of you global ambassadors, whether born in the state of Minnesota or the opposite side of the world: Don't ever stop believing and sharing. Don't ever fear that you are alone. Don't ever lose sight of the light that is yours to shine. I love each and every one of you. I am your fan. Y'all are the heroes who battle a system that forces their opinions of what is PASSING/RISING or FAILING/GET OUT. Remember that this world is about balance and that when you set your own positive goals for yourself to bring balance to the world, you outshine the trauma trying to continue to oppress us and ours.

Like one of the world's most significant rappers (and one of my faves) of all time, Tupac Shakur, said, "Reach high, for the stars lie hidden in your soul. Dream deep, for every dream precedes the goal."

We don't know what will happen tomorrow or the next day, but we do know the sun will rise and bring light. Be like that sun, South High, rise and bring yo' light! Keep the peace, y'all. Stay safe. You inspire me. Thank you for giving me the opportunity to be in your circle. To be a part of your village at South. One love y pa'lante siempre.

ACKNOWLEDGMENTS

March 16, 2020, was our last day in the classroom with the indomitable students whose words grace the book you now hold.

It was a tense day. One might have expected three classes' worth of high school students to be nonchalant, even excited about the prospect of an unexpected, extended spring break. But it was the opposite. Class periods were hushed and frenetic as students and teachers alike scrambled between last-minute instructions and assurances that things would be all right. It seemed like everyone had a tab open on their phones or laptops to Twitter or CNN. In the Writers' Room, a classroom operated by 826 MSP to offer writing and social-emotional support to students, we held a food drive because we knew so many of our students could go hungry if they couldn't come to school. At the end of every class, we told the students that we would miss them, that we would see them soon, that we loved them. We were all bracing for something that we didn't quite understand.

Worldwide pandemic aside, the three classes who wrote this book were in the homestretch of the project. We were just starting to decide what the cover would look like, what pieces would be published, how the students wanted to write their bios. And on that last day in the classroom, when going through the motions of school felt nearly pointless amidst a rising crisis, we clung to this book project not only for a shred of normalcy, but because the students knew that we were doing something important, something that would last beyond the unease of one day.

But, of course, it wasn't just one day, and the unease rose into a full-blown emergency. Two months after our last day at South High School and two miles away, George Floyd was murdered at the hands of Minneapolis Police after being suffocated for eight minutes and forty-six seconds.

As our executive director, Samantha Sencer-Mura, wrote in a statement after George Floyd's murder, "[These] events do not reflect the worlds our students dream of in their writing, nor do they reflect the place of pride when they write about home. Violence impacts our communities in a variety of ways, and this week the violence of White supremacy targeted our Black neighbors more deeply than words can say. As an organization, as community members, and as people, we cannot abide this violence. This violence reaches beyond South Minneapolis; it is codified in schools, in our government, in hiring practices, in the way history is written."

In the midst of twin pandemics of coronavirus and systemic racism, listening to Black, Indigenous youth of color like the voices in this book could not be more necessary. When COVID first arrived in the United States and Asian Americans experienced higher rates of violent hate crimes, we were already talking about dispelling Asian stereotypes and historic erasure in our classroom. When images of children in cages at the US-Mexico border were prevalent on TV, our students had already been talking about immigration and family separation. Our students were deeply engaged during discussions and readings about police brutality, gun violence, and

12

the Movement for Black Lives long before the world knew George Floyd's name, because we already knew Philando Castile, Sandra Bland, Tamir Rice, Trayvon Martin, and countless others' names. For our students, these issues are not just some intellectual thought experiment or something that just happens in the news far away. These issues affect their lives in visceral, tangible ways. We saw the impact when they had heated debates about what a Black or Brown person should do in a traffic stop, when they told us about parents and siblings in their home country whom they hadn't seen for years. Our students had so much they needed to say, so much the world needed to hear.

All this to say, yes, the 2019–20 school year brought with it far too much pain. But we would be remiss to say there wasn't also joy. Historic trauma and marginalization may impact our students' lives, but it is in no way their whole lives. They are fiercely proud of their heritages, avid soccer and basketball fans, skilled gamers, aspiring rappers, and K-pop stans. Our classes were full of jokesters who would tease you one minute and compliment your sneakers the next, all in multiple languages and with million-watt smiles. The best days were when we could share food together, whether it was donuts, burritos, fries, or sambusas. The stories would pour forth: whose mom made the best dish, who could eat the most candy, remembering when they ate that food for the first time. When we were together, we could all find comfort in and be connected by story.

In that spirit of joy and connection, we thank the following people who made this book possible:

To our dedicated team of volunteers, including Meagh Decker, Stephanie Watson, and Paul Von Drasek. With kindness, sincerity, and an ear for transcribing, you brought your full selves to each class. You could take a joke as well as dish it out, and you helped to create the culture of trust that made our classroom a safe and welcoming space to share stories. Your warm, reliable presence was dearly appreciated.

To our teaching artist, Maria Isa, who brought high energy and excellence to her every interaction with our students. You lit up the room with your presence, as you showed our BIPOC students how a successful, creative, community-driven leader could look and talk like them. In showing us your strengths, you helped us recognize ours.

To our teaching partner, Angelica Torralba-Olague, who can expertly scaffold a lesson like no other. To stand alongside you in front of a classroom, as three women of color educators centering ethnic studies and authentic experiences in every lesson, was a singular honor. You revived us with Kit Kats and Reese's, but also with your own sweetness that made your classroom a joy to be in. This was just the beginning of a beautiful friendship.

To Wise Ink Creative Publishing, especially Dara Moore Beevas and Alyssa Bluhm, the kind of partners one can only dream of yet we are lucky to have. With expertise and patience, you've mentored 826 MSP through five whole books, and more to come. The way you believe in the work of our students is a beacon that will show the way for more voices to enter the world of publishing. We could never do the Young Authors' Book Projects without you, nor would we ever want to.

To 826 MSP's committed and visionary board of directors, our squad of volunteers, and the community that continues to support us, especially the South High Foundation, the Mithun Family Foundation, the Walser Foundation, the

Maggie Foundation, 826 National, the Cuttlefish Society, the Morning Foundation, the ECMC Foundation, Cargill, the Hawkins Project, and our individual donors. Your support ensures our students' meaningful words can make their way into the world, unburdened.

OUR FAMILIES

MY FAMILY INTERVIEW

By Johnny Vasquez

My mother's words burden me

My mother's name is Maria Vasquez, and this is her story. Once my mom told me to sit down and hear what she had to say, I knew in my mind at least part of her life had to be painful to hear. She told me that she found a job at the age of eight in Ecuador, where she grew up in a two-story house she had to clean and cook 24/7. Her boss paid her well and let her sleep in a room. She saved up her money her whole life and enjoyed her job making tamales, cooking, cleaning. It was hard work for her. But she also told me that she didn't have a mother or father, but she had a sister. My mother's sister took care of her and taught her how to clean, but the sister died right before she found a job. This hurt my mother so much, but she was able to focus on work even though she cried all the time.

My mother's words burden me. When my mother finished talking about how hard she worked when she was a kid, she talked about the people she lost. She lost her father and mother in an accident, and they were the only family members my mom had during the time when she was a kid. Her sister taught her many things and also disciplined her and helped her in a way. But then her sister died unexpectedly and she was left alone with no father, no mother, not even a sister, but she pulled through it. Then, when she was in her late thirties, she got married to a person I didn't know. She loved him so much they even had a cat, a house, and everything, but then everything changed. Her husband died in a car crash and she was alone again. Then she was forced to put the cat up for adoption because she couldn't take care of it anymore. She lost her job and she felt hopeless, so she crossed the US border for a new life.

My mother's words burden me. At this point, knowing all the pain she went through saddened me, but I knew it was important for me to know, so I continued after finishing her tragic past. She told me that when she met my father in a bar, they talked and danced and got to know each other. A few months later, my dad introduced me to my new mom. She became my stepmom, but we share an intimate mother-and-son relationship. What my mom told me next was that when I was little, I ran to her with open arms around her throat and kissed her cheek, and she said by that point I stole her heart. From then on my stepmom and I spent almost all the time together. I felt happy hearing it when she told me about how she wanted my future for me. She wants me to finish high school, go to college, have a well-paying job, marry someone I love, have kids, and visit her. All I could do was smile. Hard work, dedication, perseverance, pain—here is what it takes to have value in life.

My name is **Johnny Vasquez** and I was born and raised in Saint Paul, Minnesota. I live by an okay kind of neighborhood where I can visit my friends, hang out in the park, and get to school on time. My family and I are Christian believers, and almost every Sunday or Saturday we go to church. I speak two languages, Spanish and English. My parents know very little about English, and they always call me for help if they need help reading the mail or anything that they don't understand and translating it into Spanish. I don't really like writing about myself because I get so in depth about myself that I get "distracted," but my best subject would be math because it's easy for me to understand more of it than science. My favorite food would be ramen. My favorite sport would be soccer since I grew up with it in my life. I have one sister and three older brothers; they all are grown adults, but my brothers live with my family and my sister lives in Ecuador with her four kids. I want my future career to be a uniformed officer or a K9 unit, but before I think about that I want to accomplish something my whole family hasn't done. I want to graduate from college and earn a bachelor's degree.

MY NAME

By Ikra Abdi

I was born in the year of 2005 in Ethiopia, and I traveled a lot in Somalia. My name was, however, picked by my grandpa. My name has a beautiful meaning behind it. It means *read*. When I was a little girl, my whole name was different. It was spelt in Arabic like in the English version of the Quran. It was spelled *Iqra*, but today it is spelled *Ikra*.

Growing up was difficult because I didn't speak English, so every time I looked around, people were always glaring at me. I didn't know whether or not they were talking about me. I first lived in New York, where I made many friends using my hands to talk; however, I always thought it was weird.

Although I didn't live like a wealthy person, I lived like a normal person. My parents worked a lot to provide me and my siblings a living. My parents always told me not to go outside. They were scared it was dangerous, like it was back home. I always argued with them, telling them that all people were not the same. Even though I never went outside, I looked out the window every day wondering how it was outside. It was a Thursday night when I heard my mom talking on the phone, saying that it was very dangerous out here in New York. Of course I wasn't happy.

When I told people about my name, they thought it was weird because I was obsessed with my name. My name was used a lot back in the ancient days. Our Prophet

Muhammmed (PBUH) was in danger at the time. Angel Jibril brought the Kitab or Quran to our Prophet (PBUH). The first page, or surah in Arabic, in the whole entire Quran was Iqra. My name is not only important because of the past history, but because my name is my identity and it shows who I am; I am IKRA ABDI.

My nickname is **Ikra Abdi**. I was born in Ethiopia but I was mostly raised in Tennessee. I live in a nice neighborhood with a responsible community. I can speak full Somali and a little Chinese, and I'm getting better with my Korean. I want to go to Winona State University. My future dreams are runway modeling, acting, being an entrepreneur, or maybe playing basketball.

SPECIAL ITEMS CAN BRING FAMILY TOGETHER

By Maria Clara Flores

My golden necklace looks like a small rope and it's shiny. It was given to me by my father for a religious occasion. My parents have different religions. Since my father grew up with a different religion, he gave me a spare necklace he had since he was two. And after that, it made me feel more connected with my father. Sadly, I would like to be more connected with my father's side of the family, since they are mostly all in Mexico. The last time I saw them was when I was the age of seven, but after that I haven't seen them since. My father would explain to me that my grandparents gave him the necklace, and how he was close to my grandmother. The necklace is a symbol of his and my grandmother's relationship.

So technically when my parents were young they had a type of Romeo and Juliet romance. So when my parents were neighbors, they grew up together because they attended the same school, but what was terrible was that both their parents never got along. But after some time, my mother gave birth to my brother. So after a few years, my grandmother opened up to my mother and cared for her as a daughter, since my grandfather was close with me and my older brother. We still love him and adore him. But we also bring religion here and connect with family.

I am **Maria Clara Flores**. I was born in Minnesota. I am Mexican American and I speak Spanish and English. I want other students to know that it doesn't matter what race you are. From that, anything is possible because you can accomplish any dream.

LA LLORONA

By Roselyn

The history of La Llorona (the Weeping Woman) is basically that she was the most beautiful woman of a town. Her name was Maria. There was a wealthy man roaming around, and he laid his eyes on her. He immediately fell in love with her. They eventually got to know each other and had two kids together, two boys. After some time her husband kept drifting away, and she found out he was cheating on her with someone younger and more beautiful, since her beauty was fading away. Out of rage, she drowned her kids. Realizing what she had done, she then drowned herself. She is refused entry to heaven until she finds the two souls of her sons. She now cries and takes any children that come upon her, and drowns them just like she did to her sons.

How she became an earth ghost is by killing her kids. She drowned them out of anger after finding out her husband had been unfaithful toward her and had gotten himself a younger wife. What La Llorona is doing now is killing children, having hope that two of them are her kids so she can enter the gates of heaven and live her life in peace. She is roaming the earth to kill other innocent kids to see if god or whoever is up there still lets her into heaven knowing those aren't actually her kids, and she fails every time she tries. Her kids overall I think ended up going to heaven and are living in peace right now.

My story is that my mom once told me she saw La Llorona, the Weeping Woman. She saw her on a car road coming back from the store buying some things my grandma told her to buy for supper. My mom told me she handled the situation pretty okay, feeling scared obviously, frozen into place and not knowing what to do. What she did after realizing what was in front of her was run, which everyone would have done in that situation. She went to go tell her family what happened, and her family tried to calm her down so she could tell the whole story. Her family believed her because Mexico is where La Llorona is highly likely to haunt people and to be roaming. They also told her she should be more careful going out next time.

Why is this story important to me? First, to know nothing serious actually happened to my mom and to know someone in my family experienced seeing an actual ghost in Mexico. Second, to let everyone know that she is around, warn them what they should do. Let them know what to do, that she is real and not some made-up person and story. She is dangerous and could actually hurt someone, and people are not really paying much attention to it.

So in conclusion, this legend or person is something a lot of people in Mexico believe. They don't just think she is something fake and just a story parents made up to scare their children to make them a better person or anything. She is something I would like to experience if I ever get to go to Mexico for something fun and to remember the place by. I'd like to experience something not common in the United States because things like that don't happen here.

My name is **Roselyn**. I was born and raised in Minneapolis. My ethnicity is Hispanic. I speak Spanish and English. My best subject in school is math. I have two siblings, and I live with both my parents. Right now my future career is to be a paramedic, and if not to join the army.

MY ROLE MODEL

By Carlos Gomez Vidal

My mom was born in a small town in Mexico. There was no work, so she decided to come to Minnesota at the age of twenty-nine. She came with my *tias, tia* Yadi and *tia* Ara, to start her new life. I was born March 25, 2005, in Brooklyn Center. My older brother, Pako, was born in Mexico. His real name is Francisco, but my family calls him Pako.

My mom is forty now and turns forty-one in July. She likes spending time with the family, works hard at the shampoo factory, and is a church woman, so it makes sense that the cross is so important to her. The cross is something that she has had since before I was born. Passed down from her mother to her, it is a symbol of pride and hangs in our living room above the TV. She says it is to protect us from evil spirits and keeps us safe. She wants me to go with her to church but I can't hear her when I'm sleeping.

My favorite role model is my mom. I see myself in her because she takes care of me when I'm sick. I take care of her when she's sick. We support each other.

Carlos Gomez Vidal a.k.a. Carlos the Man was born in Brooklyn Center, Minnesota. He speaks both English and Spanish. Carlos likes all types of food and any sports, but he doesn't have a future career idea yet.

MY NAME IS IMPORTANT

By Abdirahim Ibrahim

My name's important because I have the same name as my grandfather. My mom's past in Somalia was hard, so coming to America made my mom's life easier.

My mom filed a visa for me, my brothers, and my sister. Before we got our visas, we lived with other people who were waiting for their visas too. When I was born, I was named after my grandfather. I didn't know him because he died three years before in Somalia and I didn't get the chance to meet him. I know my mom had a hard life in Somalia, so when she had my brother and me it was even harder. My mom and my family moved to America to make our lives easier.

My name is Abdirahim, and that means to forgive others when they hurt you. My mom had a hard life back in Africa and had a tough experience. Coming here was a good thing for our family. We don't regret coming here but do want to visit Africa someday.

I didn't know my grandfather. He died before I could get to know him. It is good knowing my family history because maybe in the future I could go to Africa and meet people who knew my grandfather. It's also good for my kids to know about their great-grandfather even though he's not there.

My mom struggled, but through it all she is a remarkable

person. When I was born, I was named after my grandfather. It's important to me because I want to live up to my grandfather's name. My name is one of Allah's main names, and learning the meaning of forgiveness makes me a better person.

Abdirahim Ibrahim is a ninth-grade student from South High School in Minneapolis.

MY FAMILY INTERVIEW

By Osman Ibrahim

My parents came to America about twenty to twenty-five years ago, and that was after the civil war in Somalia. It was a long journey, and they have accomplished a lot in both Somalia and here. In the US, it's even better to have an opportunity, reach your goals, and succeed. The religion that my parents passed down to me helps with goals and success.

However, there is an ongoing war in Somalia and it is affecting the living conditions for most people. When my parents lived there, there was always conflict and there were not enough people working to make a positive change. There was a lot of negativity, and it stopped young people from having a safe learning environment and safe playing areas. People were shooting each other over money and power. The only thing that was left was for people to escape.

Education was very important and people in need desperately wanted to learn. That was a path that people took to get money and achieve things, but it is hard to go to school for some people because they do not have enough money. Moving here was better for education for both me and my siblings. Therefore, charity was provided to people in need, and it gave some people hope and made them feel respected and cared about. And in my opinion, the people who were shooting each other over money and power should have handled things differently for the sake of others.

All Muslims pray five times a day. Praying gets you closer to God (Allah) and you usually recite the Quran as much as you can, and if you are going through a tough time you can read a specific verse. It will most likely give you good luck.

Knowing that there is a lot of negativity in the world, like people shooting each other and government issues, my message on this is that you should always be on the positive side of things, reach goals, and do good deeds. It's very important and it could make you a better person. It can help you in many ways and reduce the wars that are affecting people.

Osman Ibrahim is a ninth-grade student from South High School in Minneapolis.

WHAT IT IS LIKE TO RAISE THREE KIDS IN DIFFERENT STATES

By Gustavo Martinez-Romero

This is about my mom's life in Mexico and the positive aspects and challenges of how she raised three kids. She had a rough life in Mexico, so she came to the US to get a better life. She had a rough life. She was the only child, so she started to work at the age of fifteen. In Mexico it was hard. There was no work, not enough food, so my mom and my grandpa were selling candy and chicharrones for five years. One day she went to the US with one of my sisters. She went over there for family and she stayed in California.

She came back to Mexico for my grandpa, but he passed away one night. So then she had my other sis. My mom stayed a little bit in Mexico, then went back to the US, then she stayed in Chicago with her friend. Then she thought of going to Minnesota because of my uncle, so then my mom moved over there, and a couple years later she had me.

I am **Gustavo Martinez-Romero.** I have two dogs. My chihuahua, Pelitos, she's not friendly. She won't even smell you. She just freaks out. My yorkie, Mechitas, scares really easily.

She just is quiet and eats everything. I live in a house near a park. It's a pretty big park. The park people that work there are really nice. I like planting plants with my mom. I don't even know what they're called, but we've got a lot of plants. Got a baby cactus and a really big cactus. On Saturdays I feed my dog and make myself something to eat. Something that's good. We go to Walmart and we get eggs, potatoes, and bacon and sausages and popcorn chicken nuggets, and I will eat that in the morning. I do chores for Mama. Some Saturdays I'm a little lazy and I don't wanna clean up. I am a part of my family and friends.

WHO MURDERED MY GRANDFATHER?

By Akrama Mursal

Although I never met him, my grandfather is a really important person to me. I want to learn more about him because he died when my dad was really young. When my grandfather was still alive, he was a hardworking man providing food and clothing and a home for his family.

Before my grandfather died, he was a healthy young man. He was the only person who had a job and worked for the family and paid the bills and everything else. My grandfather would read the Quran for my dad and his other siblings and take them to dugsi and teach them how to pray and tell them stories about our prophets.

The struggles my dad's family went through after my grandfather's death were paying the bills and getting food and providing shelter for themselves. For this reason, they had to stay at friends' homes because they got kicked out of their house, and they had to move away because there was a war.

My dad's family changed after my grandfather's death. He never got justice and my family never got justice for his murder. When they were in Mogadishu, there was war and people were trying to take over Mogadishu. My grandfather went there and the government shot him because he was on the liberal side.

To summarize, my grandfather was a nice man and a hard-working man who was religious and got killed for being on the liberal side. I will always remember him.

Akrama Mursal is a ninth-grade student from South High School in Minneapolis.

MY FAMILY INTERVIEW

By Cruz Navarrete Angelito

Tamales remind me of early youth in Mexico. My grandmother taught my mother to make them. And eventually I began to learn to make them myself.

My family was living in Mexico, where my father died when I was eight months old. After that, my mom needed money so we could eat. My grandma was taking care of us.

Shortly after, my mom moved to the US to work. When she came to the US, she moved to Nebraska. When she had my little brother Kevin, she moved to Minnesota. Ten years later, when I was eleven, I joined her in Minnesota. Four of my brothers and sisters are here with me, and two more are in Mexico.

Cruz Navarrete Angelito is a ninth-grade student at South High School in Minneapolis.

WHAT WAS IT LIKE TO IMMIGRATE TO THE UNITED STATES?

By Luis Rojas Garcia

When talking to my dad about this, he wasn't really sure if he wanted to share his story. He told me he didn't want to share his story because of what he had been through, but he shared and his story was interesting. My dad is from Mexico and came to the US for a better life. My dad works in fixing people's yards or something like that. He's close with mainly his family. My dad has one daughter and one son, including me. My dad describes himself as a hardworking person who makes sure we do good in school. My dad didn't have these types of opportunities in his life, and he says that kids nowadays take opportunities for granted. My dad was around my age when he came to the US.

It's important to know your parents' story of how they came to the US to give us opportunities they didn't really have. It was good talking to my dad because I asked similar questions to him when I was younger, and it made me realize how when you talk to your parents it's different from when you talk to others.

Luis Rojas Garcia is a ninth-grade student at South High School in Minneapolis.

MY MOM

By Pakia Vang

My mom was born in Laos. When she lived in Laos, she didn't have to go to school because there wasn't a school for her to go to. So she stayed home and helped her parents, and did chores like washing clothes, washing the dishes, and cooking food. She also went to a farmland with her family, and she also had lots of friends in Laos too. Then she moved to Thailand, and stayed over there for four or five years, and also went to school and studied in Thailand. She also moved to other places with her family.

When she came to America, it was hard for her because she didn't know how to speak English, so my family had some help from someone who knew how to speak Hmong and English. For us Hmong people, we sometimes wear a Buddha's necklace to protect us from having nightmares. When we celebrate Hmong New Year, it's like where we have big celebrations and give thanks to our ancestors for the completion of the Harvest's Year.

My name is **Pakia Vang**. I have four brothers and I'm the youngest in the family. I live with my mom and my brothers, and my father has passed away. My future career is becoming a businesswoman and doing business stuff. I'm still deciding if I should go to college or not.

FAMILY INTERVIEW

By Khalid Wadi

Are you human? Are you sure? OK.

Then we all have families. Some we choose, some we were born into, and some of us are still searching, but we all come from family at some point. Love is what makes families, families.

My family heirloom is a tasbih and dates back to my grandfather. It is a religious thing. Tasbih in English roughly translates to amulet.

My tasbih gives me pride and makes me proud of my history and my family. Having the heirloom gives me a connection to my heritage. The passing of the tasbih started when my grandfather gave it to his wife, my grandma, Riquiya. My grandma gave it to her eldest son, my uncle, Khader. He and I have some things in common. Khader, myself, and my little brother Nuredin are the only darkskins in my family. But my brother isn't tall like my uncle and I are tall. Well, I'm pretty tall, or I consider myself tall—one more inch and I'd be six feet. The tasbih passed from my uncle to his sister, my hooyo, who gave it to me when I was eleven.

The opportunity to have something that belonged to my ancestors makes me feel like I have a connection to them, and that amulet is part of who I am. Having something physical that I can touch gives me pride and lets me know that I have people who care about me because the tasbih connects me to my past and future.

In conclusion, having the necklace gives me pride to be related to my grandfather and connects me with my family. The family that I was born into made me proud of who I am and where I come from. The family that I choose inspires me and motivates me to be the best me I can be. All or nothing.

My name is **Khalid Wadi**. I was born in Ethiopia but I was raised in America. I live in the Powderhorn neighborhood. My ethnicity is Somali or African, African American. A lot of things apply to me related to race. I speak English and Somali. I hope my writing displays my personality: funny, honest, calm, emotionally strong, and a free spirit who is determined too.

OUR LANGUAGES

MY MOTHER'S ENGLISH

By Ikra Abdi

There was always a rich side and a poor side in Africa. While my dad studied and took four years of college, my mom on the other hand washed dishes and fed us. I wish my mom could experience what going to school is like, and communicating. Sometimes I say stuff in English instead of Somali. My mother goes "aa-aah" in Somali, meaning "huh." She goes, "Don't forget your language, it's part of your identity. It's like keeping your passport."

My mother's English is like hail hitting your car screen on a cold day, "BOOM" like thunder from a windy day. "Brrrrr," my mom goes, like Nicki Minaj's hit "MotorSport." My mom gives me a body language, meaning she is about to tell me something. She goes, "Little girl, lose your attitude before you lose your culture."

The day before fourth grade starts, I get up for school, wearing my headscarf. However, I don't want to. I want my hair in pigtails that I can flip side to side like the fair-skin, silky black-haired Korean girls. I can hear the "NO" before my mom even opens her lips.

I knew I had to find myself in life, and when I did, it felt like an empowering moment, like the moment of truth on a court day. I wanted my hair shown, trust me, but I couldn't because god gave me a present: the hijab.

MY NATIVE LANGUAGE

By Maria Clara Flores

My native language is something I'm proud of because in the future, if I want to do something I enjoy doing, I'll be able to earn more money for being able to speak more than one language. So it will make me happy because I'll be able to support my family in whatever they need help in.

And when I'm working I'll be remembering my mother's words, telling me "Maria, lava los trastes." I would say, "Y yo porque." But afterwards I would go ahead and do them.

And going somewhere and telling family and friends while eating, "Buen provecho," and them responding back with "Gracias." Going off to get food with my family, and getting some tamales and champurrado and wondering where to sit at when there's no place to sit.

And remembering how friends and family call me "chapra" and asking my mom why my height is smaller than other girls' my age and her telling me it's not, I'm just unique. I'm the limited edition of other girls.

MY LANGUAGE

By Fahima Dahir

My culture is based on how you speak,
It's like a rainy day without the rainbow at the end, it's just gloomy and sad.
My mother always said, if u step out of a plane speaking like that, u might as well cry ur way back inside.
My family says the same things to the little one, the more chuckles in the air the more cracks in their voices.
I said to my older cousin, "Maxay muhiim u tahay in la barto Soomaaliga?" She said back, "la'aanteed afkeenna ma jiri doontid."

Translation: *I said to my older cousin, "Why do I have to learn Somali?" She said back, "Without our language, you would not exist."*

Fahima Dahir is a ninth-grade student at South High School in Minneapolis.

HAPPY NEW YEAR

By Hawi

መልካም አዲስ ዓመት
Happy new year
Everyone says it on New Year's
It means happy new year
It symbolizes respect

My name is **Hawi** and I was born and raised in Ethiopia. Now I live in Minnesota. I speak two languages, English and Amharic, and I can understand Oromo but I can't speak it. I don't exactly know what my writing is supposed to say about me, but I guess it says that I'm a writer. My hobbies are drawing, cooking, and playing video games (sometimes). My favorite foods are Chipotle, pizza, pasta, and fried chicken. My favorite desserts would be ice cream, cake, and cookies. My favorite sport is basketball. A message I want to send to other people who speak two or more languages is to never forget them, and to be proud of them, as well. I have one brother and I live with my mom.

OREO AND CHICLE

By Carlos Gomez Vidal

My Spanish is like my favorite ice cream blend: Oreo and chicle. I put the chicle at the bottom and Oreo at the top. My Spanish is like chicle because it is fun to blow, it pops, and it gives me joy. My English is like Oreo because I eat it every day just like I use my English every day.

Sometimes in my home we speak Spanish, sometimes English, and many times both. My mom tells me in Spanish, "Por te bien en es escuela." I tell her back, "OK, Mom, I will be good." When I get home, I always see her cook and ask her, "What are you cooking?" She doesn't need to tell me because I know she is making one of my favorites, eggs.

I like it when my mom tells me, "Ten cuidado." I say, "OK, Ma, I will." At night, when my mom wants to go to sleep and I'm still playing Xbox, she tells me, "Vete dormir," and when I don't get off my Xbox, she throws her chancla at me. She yells at me sometimes, but I know the power of the chancla.

MY LANGUAGE

By Luis Rojas Garcia

My Spanish is a mix of English and Spanish. When I talk to my dad, it's always me searching for some words I don't know because my Spanish isn't that great. The one thing my dad tells me most of the time is, "Adonde esta la novia," and I just laugh. My dad's Spanish is perfect, but when English comes right at the corner he doesn't know much. But still he puts in effort to at least understand and somewhat speak it. An English phrase he says is, "What time is it." A funny thing my dad likes to do is mock me and my sister's Spanish, but mostly my sister's, because she still needs work on speaking it.

LO QUE IMPORTA ES COMO SOY YO

By Roselyn

My Spanish is not perfect or good,
Parents get mad when I talk English at home
Although it's really not my fault, really.
Wondering if I ever will get better at my language.
Mi familia y yo no somos ricos como otros,
Pero tenemos lo que necesitamos.
Y tampoco mi familia es la más perfecta.
También somos como el resto del mundo.
Having fights and other types of stuff.
But we all end up getting through it together.
Mi familia siempre me decía que no era como
Las otras niñas por mi nombre.
Pero recuerdo que otras también tienen mi nombre.
Y también me dicen que el nombre no importa
Lo que importa es como soy yo.

MY LANGUAGE

By Pakia Vang

My language is Hmong, and when I'm at home, I speak Hmong to my mom because she doesn't know English. Whenever we go shopping, she says to ask one of the workers to help us find what we're looking for. Sometimes when she says something to me in Hmong and in English, her accent in English is very confusing and funny because she doesn't know how to speak in English. And when my mom says something in Hmong like "Npaj zaub mov lawm," it means that like food is ready.

AMHARIC

By Soly

ለእጄ ውጋ ውሰጀ means to bring water to my hand.
Elders
Before eating lunch and after
Respect
It symbolizes blessing

My name is **Soly**. I was born in an Ethiopian country called Jimma. I speak Amharic. My writing explains Ethiopan culture and tradition. My hobbies are mostly playing soccer and drawing or singing sometimes. For me the best subject is history because it teaches us about histories that happened before we were born. My favorite food is injera bewet—that's Ethiopan traditional food. I want people to know everybody has their own culture and it's all important. I have two brothers and I live with my mom and dad. I want to be a good lawyer and model. I don't know what college I want to go to yet, but probably in the Twin Cities because I don't want to go far from my family.

LIKE PAPER THAT IS RIPPED

By F. MUSSA

My mom says to me, "Maal gotu girta"
And I tell her, "Mama, you see, you see what I'm doing?"
She replies back, "Okay"
Just an African thing every parent does

My Oromo is like paper that is ripped,
Worthless
I really can't speak it
But I understand
My family speaks English more than Oromo

Parents always say how are you going to speak to your grand-
parents? ("Akami adada kaati dubita?")
I say I can do it.
Not that hard to speak, I just don't feel like it
My parents always say my Oromo was the best when I was four.
They would sometimes say my Oromo was better than theirs.
School got me speaking English only.
They say to me, "Mana baramso oromo kaati kakabsay."

My name is **F. MUSSA**. I was born and raised in Minneapolis.
I live in the Augsburg College area. I am African American. I
speak Oromo at home. But I also speak English everywhere

54

I go. Even at home all we speak is English. I can write a lot without breaks. I like playing basketball. My favorite subject is math. My favorite food is pizza and fries. I have siblings. I live with my parents. I want to start my own business or make it to the NBA.

MY MAMA'S ENGLISH

By Stephanie Ponce Delgado

My mama's English is like a warm day during a Minnesota winter month.
When my mama gets mad she uses her inglés against us.
My mama will always be that one strong and independent person I will always admire.
My mom would tell me "Lava los trastes"
and I would be like "No"
and she would be mad at me
and she would tell me "No te voy a hablar otra vez"
or she would tell my sister "Traime el cinturon"
by then I knew I had to wash the dishes
or do whatever she said
or else she would get mad.

My name is **Stephanie Ponce Delgado**. I was born and raised in South Minneapolis. I went to two different schools when my family and I moved to Texas. We traveled often between Texas and Minnesota to see family and friends. I moved back to Minnesota to start high school in Minneapolis at South High School. I am Mexican American. I speak two languages, Spanish and English, and I am currently learning Korean. I want people to know that speaking other languages is not easy, because some words in other languages may mean something different in another language. I have one older sister and three younger than me, and a baby that is coming soon. I live with my mom. For my future college, I want to attend school in South Korea, and my career is undecided.

OUR
LIVES

FIRST TIME I REALIZED I WAS MUSLIM

By Abdirahim Ibrahim

I first realized I was Islamic when I was five. My mom was praying and I asked what she was doing. Then after she was done she said that in our culture we have to pray five times a day, so I didn't understand at first. Then two years later, I learned how to pray and read the Quran. I was unsure what my mom was talking about, but later I understood and I felt happy that I knew that I'm part of that culture.

HISTORY

By Fahima Dahir

I'm a street in front of a bodega,
Seeing thugs moving so foolishly,
Seeing precious kids turning depressed
Cuz of them witnessing
They brother dead
On me
Oh how this world turned so grumpy
Feeling blood dripping through my cracks,
Feeling earthquakes when shots go off,
Seeing gang members looking so furiously,
Seeing teenagers being so helplessly
So they can take that blue pill
So they can feel so smoothly

BE PROUD OF WHO YOU ARE

By Hawi

Be proud of who you are
Let your hairstyle complement your beauty
Be proud of who you are
Have pride in your skin color
Rise my Black queens and kings
Put your crown back on
Be proud of who you are

MOTHER NATURE

By Hawi

Mother Nature
I care, I love, I give to my children
When it's too dark for them
I call upon the sun
When it's too bright for them
I call upon the clouds
I give them all I have
The rain, the sunlight
To grow all the crops they need
I never ask nothing in return
Expect for love and care
And look at me now
My own children turned their
Backs on me

So when the thunderstorm
Comes do not call for me
For this is all your doing

STRAY

By Santiago Mendoza

I'm just like a dog getting hurt
and a stray
always alone
nowhere to go
no food no home
people hurt me because
they don't like what I do
and I just wanted to be loved
and be in a nice
Family

MY FIRST EXPERIENCE WITH MY RACIAL IDENTITY

By Santiago Mendoza

When I went to a Mexican party, my dad was speaking Spanish and drinking. My mom was watching telenovelas. We went to Mexico. I noticed that I was caramel and not white like the rest of the school in pre-K.

Santiago Mendoza is a ninth-grade student at South High School in Minneapolis.

SCHOLARSHIP

By Soly

School
Calm as a turtle
Helpful to others
Open with family
Live
Argument
Rule you need to follow
Sad as rainy day
Happy as a panda
Intelligence
Peaceful

DON'T GIVE UP

By Soly

Don't give up
Think positive and don't be absent
Don't give up
I work to get diploma
That make my future bright
To change the laziness
Don't give up be strong and work hard

GUN THAT DOESN'T WANT TO SHOOT

By Abdihakim Muhumud

I'm a gun that doesn't want to kill people.
I wish the man would not shoot.
I wish he could run out of ammo.
I can feel the pressure inside.
I can tell he doesn't want to shoot.
But he shoots.
I can hear people screaming

Abdihakim Muhumud is a ninth-grade student at South High School in Minneapolis.

MY HIJAB

By Akrama Mursal

I am a warm covering for young
women
who follow their religion.
Other people that don't believe in Islam would call me a
"scarf"
Some people make fun of me saying that
women
only wear it to cover the fact that they're bald
But they only make themselves look dumb.
I would never judge a
girl
wearing a tube top in the summer.
Don't judge people's identity

PEOPLE THAT ARE THERE FOR ME

By F. Mussa

My parents love when I do well
My neighbors are there to watch me
My teachers are there to support me
My cousins are there to comfort me
My teachers are there to help me get better
I speak Oromo and English at home
My friends speak English at home

THIS LAND WAS MADE FOR YOU AND ME

By Cruz Navarrete Angelito

This land was made for you and me,
they may have guns but we are still here,
we are terrified to be killed and separated,
open the border and let us in faster,
families are apart,
this land was made for you and me.

IMMIGRATION / DEPORTATION

By Stephanie Ponce Delgado

In a car there is a person trying to get to work. He is happy, well. Goodbye to his daughters, he said less. He knows it was his last goodbye. There he goes waiting for the red light to turn into a green light. Once it turns to green, he tries to turn. Once he sees blue and red lights and hears a siren, he stops and waits. Police search his car and he has no license nor insurance. Police take him, his phone stays in the car. His wife is really worried. At 3:00 p.m., she gets a phone call not knowing who it was. She answers the phone. It is her husband. Both in tears, speaking and trying to find ways to get him out. But at last, off he goes on an adventure to his homeplace where he was born. That car is left with his wife and she sells it to not have any memory of what happened to her husband with that car.

SOFT PILLOW

By Khalid Wadi

I am fluffy,
soft,
trusting,
pretty, peaceful, happy

In the afternoon they
come and let all the sadness go and throw it at me,

but what about mine
After they're done they leave, sad, so I sit there all lonely

and showering in the sadness
Sadness becomes my water, without anyone, but they seem
happy, so I sit there happy for what I've done for the humans,

but what do I know I'm just a pillow.

BE PROUD

By Maria Isa

South High
Southside Minneapolis
Twin Cities
The Whole World
Todo el Mundo

Be proud of who you are
We living for tomorrow and today
Be proud of who you are
You can't break us
You can't take us away
Be proud of who you are
'Cause we gonna make it
We gonna make it our way
Be proud of who you are
'Cause you can't break us
You can't break us away
Be proud of who you are
Be proud of who you are

Were the streets in front of bodegas
And we know our history
We have pride in where we come from
And how we've been surviving

We are proud of our native tongues
Proud daughters and proud sons

Through the greed of wars and weapons
Evils that envy, powers that be
We continue to fight for love
Live for the ancestry
We just want to wake with the sun
We don't want to hear the guns pop off
We've had enough

Tenemos orgullo
Es como soy yo, como soy yo
Por lo mío y lo tuyo
lo que importa,
Es como soy yo
Tenemos orgullo
Es como soy yo, como soy yo
Por lo mío y lo tuyo
lo que importa,
Es como soy yo
Tenemos orgullo
Es como soy yo, como soy y
Por lo mío y lo tuyo
lo que importa,
Es como soy yo

Be proud of who you are
We living for tomorrow and today
Be proud of who you are
You can't break us
You can't take us away

Be proud of who you are
'Cause we gonna make it
We gonna make it our way
Be proud of who you are
'Cause you can't break us
You can't break us away
Be proud of who you are
Be proud of who you are

We don't wanna hear the guns pop off
You don't wanna hear the guns pop off

We don't wanna hear the guns pop off
You don't wanna hear the guns pop off

We don't wanna hear the guns pop off
You don't wanna hear the guns pop off

We don't wanna hear the guns pop off
We just wanna be with mama, we just wanna be with papa
We just wanna be with our homies
We just wanna be with our blocks

We don't wanna hear the guns pop off
You don't wanna hear the guns pop off
We don't wanna hear the guns pop off

"Be Proud" is a song written and performed by teaching artist Maria Isa. The lyrics were inspired by the pieces created by the students featured in this book. To hear the song and download it for yourself, go to soundcloud.com/826msp/be-proud

APPENDIX

A NOTE FROM THE TEACHER

By Angelica Torralba-Olague

It has been such a pleasure to work as an Academic Language Development (ALD) teacher for my English Learners (ELs) for the 2019–2020 school year. I've seen the students grow from being hesitant to write in the beginning of the year to writing their own personal books or poems at home towards the end of the year. The turning point was when the students prepared for and conducted interviews with their family members in November and December of 2019. Oral storytelling is something that is so common in our students' lives. Writing their family's immigrant story, a family memory, or an aspect of their culture that's been passed down is translating the power of oral stories onto paper. There was a sense of deeper understanding of self, affirmation of identity, and safety in their community—key ingredients that help students thrive, excel, and become independent in their learning.

The result of the family interview project allowed for us to authentically discuss tougher subjects together when we returned from break, creating poems and works of art as a way to turn pain to purpose. Writing for justice for their fellow classmate and friend who was shot and killed by the police. Writing to dismantle the internalized oppression that has developed from years of discrimination based on their accent, language, race, religion, or gender. Not needing to code switch but loving themselves for exactly who they are and accepting themselves and others in whatever form they come in every day. Lastly, writing for peace, for understanding, and for positivity in this world.

As a former EL student myself, this book project is not only a professional endeavor but a very personal one. I immigrated to Minneapolis when I was six years old and attended MPS schools. Like many of the students who may have been brought to the United States at a younger age, I too have felt that disconnect of feeling distant from my own culture and language and yet being reminded of those differences every day. Although I have felt this for many years, I didn't get an opportunity to really reflect on it until my time at St. Olaf College as an American racial and multicultural studies (now called ethnic studies) major. As an EL teacher today, I am grateful to have the opportunity to reach out to students and welcome them as ninth graders in this way. My hope is that they can continue to write to strengthen their understanding of self and their family; that they continue the rest of their high school years developing their skill to ask critical questions when they may not feel seen or heard.

I am appreciative of the partnership with 826 MSP, their staff, and their volunteers! It has been valuable to co-plan, work with students individually and in small groups, and debrief the lessons and student support weekly. It has been powerful to work with staff and with a program that shares the importance of co-creating with students and centering their own stories and experiences in each lesson.

EDUCATOR RESOURCES

LESSON: "Inheritance," a family interview project

3 Sessions, 1 Hour Each

Goals and Core Curriculum Standards:

- **Literary Analysis:** Determine a central idea of a text and analyze its development over the course of the text, including how it emerges and is shaped and refined by specific details.

- **Narrative Writing:** Develop real experiences or events using effective technique and well-chosen details and by engaging and orienting the reader through observation, establishing one or multiple point(s) of view, introducing characters, and creating a smooth progression of experiences or events.

- **Interpersonal Communication:** Working in small groups, developing questions, and conducting interviews.

Materials: Butcher paper and/or large poster board, markers, enough copies of short stories and articles for students to read or share.

The concept of inheritance can encompass far more than material wealth. Everything from the way we speak to how we carry ourselves, how we look, gestures, recipes, garments, jewelry, religious practices, names—we can trace these things back to the people who raised us.

Behind every thing or trait we inherit is a story, a story that can connect us back to ancestors we may never even have had the chance to meet. This lesson endeavors to preserve some of those stories among your students' families through an interviewing activity and a narrative essay.

Over the course of a minimum of three sessions, students will identify something they have inherited from their families, learn how to conduct interviews about that inheritance with their families, and write a narrative essay about what they learned in those interviews. More sessions can be added to scaffold or expand portions as your students need.

This lesson is especially well suited for English Language Learners, as it encompasses skills building in reading, writing, speaking, and listening. Students begin this project by reading and analyzing mentor texts to model their own narratives after. They then watch and listen to examples of successful interviews, develop and write their own interview questions to speak with their family members, and finally combine all their learnings into a creative narrative project. An optional final step is to encourage the students to recite and record their final narratives for additional speaking practice.

But perhaps the most rewarding part of this whole project is the opportunity for students to learn more about where they came from, to preserve a piece of their history or culture, and in doing so have the ability to assert unequivocally that their history and culture matter. For the students who participated in this book project, all of whom hail from immigrant families, that preservation and assertion was monumentally important. Many students reported that they learned things in conversation with their families that they had never heard before, and that the interview process made them feel closer to their loved ones.

Additionally, too often the white supremacist culture so dominant in the United States labels the contributions of immigrants as too strange, too weird, too foreign, too exotic, too other to be worthy of a place in the history books. With this project, our students push back and prove that their families' narratives deserve pride of place in books just like this one.

These materials were developed by 826 MSP's program director, Cristeta Boarini, based on the high school Academic Language Development curriculum of our partner teacher, Angelica Torralba-Olague.

SESSION 1: WHAT DOES "INHERITANCE" MEAN?

Preparation

For English Language Learners, the idea of "inheritance" (and especially a more expanded definition to include all cultural artifacts and stories from one's ancestors) might be a new one. We started off this session with a warm-up writing question: What's the best gift you ever received and why was it the best? This question helps to frame the concept of inheritance as something positive. We then took a few minutes to define inheritance, and to point out words with similar roots including:

- Inherit
- Heir
- Heirloom
- Heritage

With this grounding, students were better prepared to brainstorm ideas for their inheritance topics.

Reviewing a Mentor Text (45 mins)

Before embarking on any writing project journey, it is crucial to offer students a variety of mentor texts to model their writing after. Mentor texts should not only showcase the writing techniques you hope your students can utilize, but should also be representative of the students' identities. Too often, an outdated or culturally insensitive mentor text can leave a student more confused after analyzing the text than before they started, because not only do they have to understand the techniques showcased, but they may also struggle to decode the cultural references as well.

During this project, our students read through the following mentor texts and answered discussion questions to explore the concept of inheritance. The texts specifically related to shared identities of students in our classes:

1. "Coin Belts" by Juliet Xiong, an essay from 826 MSP's 2017 publication *Adventures Within Another*. This essay was written by a high school student who identifies as Hmong. In the essay, the writer articulates why the coin belts of her Hmong cultural clothes are important to her. This offered students a prime example of "inheritance" as a cultural object. Discussion questions included:
  - Why are coin belts important to the writer?
  - What do coin belts symbolize or represent?

2. "Tamalada" by David Bowles, a chapter from his 2018 book

They Call Me Güero. This chapter includes many concepts we wanted to showcase to the students, such as the beauty of bilingual writing and the concept of "inheritance" as recipes, stories, or sayings passed down in a family. Discussion questions for this text included:

- What examples can you find of things that have been passed down in Güero's family?
- What does this story remind you of in your life? Visualize an example and note all the little details.

As part of the Academic Language Development curriculum for this group of English Language Learners, students learned the Cornell Notes strategy. While reading the mentor texts, students were encouraged to underline and annotate based on examples where they could Connect, Visualize, Question, Respond, and Summarize.

Developing Word Banks (15 mins)

Set three sheets of butcher paper or poster board around the classroom with markers easily accessible. Each paper should be labeled with one of the following questions:

- What gets passed down?
- Who passes things down?
- Why is it important to pass things down?

Divide the class into small groups, with each group starting at a different question. Encourage the students to write down words that they associate with each question. These topics should evoke a strong response for students. Allow them to self-identify as much as possible, rather than supplying ideas. There are no wrong answers, but they should be honest answers. After four to five minutes at each station, have the small groups rotate.

Once all the students have rotated through, the lists they have made will likely reveal their values, beliefs, and loves. Many classmates may find similarities that can spark conversation. It's a simple but energizing activity.

These questions and words associated with them will serve as word banks for the students as they continue to develop interview questions for their families and write their narratives. If ever they are stuck or lacking inspiration, direct them to the word banks. The posters can continue to be hung around the classroom or transcribed into handouts for student reference.

After this thorough investigation of the concept of inheritance, students should begin thinking about something they themselves have inherited in their lives. The inheritance might be an object, saying, story, or custom. While delivering this lesson, it is important to be mindful that not all students are in contact with their families. For this reason, we opened up the project to include "inherited" items from any mentors, coaches, or role models who have influenced the students' lives. No student should be made to feel like they cannot participate due to their family situation.

SESSION 2: WHAT MAKES A GOOD INTERVIEW?

Preparation

Before students interview their families about their "inheritance" topic, they need to be prepared to host a fruitful conversation. Creating productive interview questions and conducting an interview that leaves all parties feeling seen and heard takes practice. This session offers multiple ways for students to test their skills!

For this lesson, the educator gets to be a bit of an actor. Before the class, prep a really simple topic to conduct a mock interview with a volunteer. In our classes, we held the session at the end of November, so our topic was Thanksgiving traditions. By hosting a mock interview, you will be able to demonstrate to the students good and bad interviewing techniques.

Demonstrating a Mock Interview (15 mins)

Once you've landed on a simple interview topic and a willing volunteer, instruct the class to take note of everything you, the educator, do wrong over the course of the interview. The educator should take the role of the interviewer, the volunteer will be the interviewee.

There are a variety of bad interview techniques you can demonstrate. Don't be afraid to get emphatic and silly as you act these out:

- Pretend to show up late
- Intentionally mess up the interviewee's name
- Avoid eye contact
- Interrupt the interviewee
- Ask only yes or no questions (e.g., Do you like mashed potatoes?)
- Be on your phone throughout the interview
- Look obviously bored (big sighs, slumped in chair)

- Do not take notes
- Ask questions that are off topic

Essentially, all these tactics exhibit rudeness or carelessness—behaviors no one wants to experience when they're talking about a personal and meaningful topic. Once you've acted through a few of these excruciating behaviors, ask the class how you as the interviewer could do better. Take their suggestions into account and redo the interview, this time exhibiting much better interview behavior including:

- Explain to the interviewee the project you're working on and the types of questions you'll ask
- Ask permission to take notes and/or record the interview on your phone for future reference
- Make positive eye contact
- Ask open-ended questions using who, what, when, where, why, and how
- If the interviewee says something interesting, ask them a follow-up question on the same topic
- Sit up straight, nod, and emote to show active listening
- The last question should be "Is there anything you would like to add?" to give the interviewee an opportunity to share something you may have missed
- After a few good questions, thank the interviewee for the time

After the second mock interview, ask the class what things went better. You can even encourage the volunteer to share their experience between the two different interview styles. This exercise will show students that the types of questions they ask, their body language, and their preparedness will dramatically change the quality of the answers they receive from their interviewee.

While the mock interview shows drastic differences, students might find it more difficult to conceptualize the good interview traits in a real-life situation. That's why we watched a wonderful interview that *The Daily Show* host Trevor Noah filmed with his grandmother in South Africa (available on YouTube). For this project, most students were interviewing family members that they knew quite well. The respectful, loving, and oftentimes silly conversation between Noah and his grandma acted as almost a preview of what the students could hope for from their own family interviews.

Developing Solid Interview Questions (20 mins)

At the core of a good interview is a great conversation. With a solid set of prepared, thought-provoking questions, anyone can excel at an interview that will lead to beautiful stories.

To start our question development, we encouraged students to discuss what goes into a question that would spark a meaningful answer. Lumen Learning has an excellent, free online article titled "Writing Effective Interview Questions" that our classes studied together. The article explains that the best interview questions are always:

- Relevant
- Open-Ended
- Clear
- Applicable
- Unbiased

Making a Plan (25 mins)

At this point, students should have a firmer grasp of ideas regarding something they've inherited from their families, as well as effective interview strategies. Either in a class journal or on a graphic organizer, ask the students to make a plan to prepare for their upcoming family interviews.

1. Articulate potential interview topic ideas such as
   - Recipes or foods my family eats or makes a lot
   - Stories my family tells all the time
   - Cultural or religious traditions that my family does that are important to us

2. Write interview questions
   - Students should identify who they intend to interview

3. Plan or schedule a time to interview a family member or mentor about the topic
   - Students should decide how they will record or take notes about the interview

We encouraged the students to conduct their interviews over winter break so that by the time the students returned to school they would have the stories and information they needed to begin the final part of the project: writing.

SESSION 3: PUTTING IT ALL TOGETHER

With interview notes or a recording transcription in hand, students should be ready to begin the writing process. Our classes began by outlining a standard five-paragraph essay format with an introduction (including a hook and main idea or thesis), three body paragraphs, and a conclusion. Two techniques that our students were specifically tasked with including in their narrative essays were a strong use of descriptive language, as well as transitions to flow between paragraphs.

If the students recorded their interview with their family, a key step is to transcribe the conversation. Depending on the student, transcription can be a challenge. However, it is an excellent way to practice typing and listening. Since the student already participated in the interview, they should be familiar with the contents of the recording, thus making the transcription process more manageable.

Future follow-up sessions can include peer review, revising drafts, or even reading essays aloud and recording. The latter step was well received by our students, who turned their recordings into videos that included pictures of the foods, heirlooms, religious artifacts, and various other things that were important to their families' stories.

When our students finished this project, their pride was palpable. For many of our ninth graders, they had never written a piece of such length. Several students told us that the writing came easily because for the first time in a while (if ever), they were able to write about something they cared about deeply. To find student examples from this heartwarming and culturally connected project, refer to the essays in the first section of this book, under "Our Families."

ABOUT THE SCHOOL

South High School is a public high school that serves nearly two thousand students in Minneapolis. The school has a tradition of excellence in academic, artistic, and athletic achievement. South has three academic programs: All Nations, Liberal Arts, and Open. All programs provide core programming and preparation for college and opportunities beyond high school.

South is also a school that serves high-needs populations, with rates of free and reduced lunch above 50 percent, and 25 percent or more of the student population is classified as English Language Learners. In March of 2020, South High pivoted to a full distance learning model in light of the COVID-19 pandemic, a model which persisted through the 2020–21 school year.

The students who created this book speak a variety of languages, including Somali, Spanish, Amharic, Oromo, and Hmong.

ABOUT THE EDUCATORS

Angelica Torralba-Olague is licensed in English as a Second Language (ESL). She has taught a variety of EL classes for newcomers to long-term ELs. She published *Immigrant Stories*, an anthology of stories of her newcomer students, in 2019, when she taught an EL writing class for levels 1 and 2. Angelica also teaches AVID 9.

Cristeta Boarini is a journalist and storyteller based in South Minneapolis. Originally from the Chicagoland area, Cristeta graduated cum laude from the University of Minnesota in 2011. Boarini's entire professional career has focused on amplifying marginalized voices across Minnesota. She won First Place from the Inland Press Association in 2013 and the Minnesota Newspaper Association in 2014 for her reporting. Cristeta's writing has been featured in local media outlets such as the *bMag* (Bush Foundation), *The Growler Magazine*, and *Twin Cities Daily Planet*. Cristeta currently serves on the board of the Metropolitan Regional Arts Council. In her role as 826 MSP's program director, Boarini oversees 826 MSP's six main areas of programming, including Storytelling & Bookmaking Field Trips, the Writers' Room, Creative Writing Workshops, After-School Writing Lab, Young Authors Book Project, and Young Authors' Council.

Jeannine Erickson is Washington-born but Minnesota-raised and has lived here for the last nineteen years. She is a recent graduate of St. Catherine University with a BA in critical studies of race and ethnicity and French and currently works as the writers' room manager at South High School. Jeannine shares how all the magic moments that took place while working this project made the writing and this work so liberating. "It's the students, our partner teacher Angelica Olague, the teaching artists, our team; each of us adding our own flavor to the secret sauce that makes this anthology so heartfelt, true, and timely." For those who are looking for their own scripture, their own truth, their own story, and the stories yet to be told, she invites them to dive deep into *Words Unburden Me*. Jeannine adds, echoing the words of the featured teaching artist Maria Isa and student Hawi: Be proud of who you are.

Maria Isa Pérez-Hedges is a Boricua singer, songwriter, actress, rapper, activist, youth worker, and international recording artist born in Minnesota and raised on St. Paul's West Side barrio. She was raised by the influences of many different rhythms of Afro-Latino-Indigenous culture and channeled it into performing arts and activism at a very early age. Isa has been trained by the masters of the Afro-Boricua Diaspora from the island of Puerto Rico (Paracumbe, Tito Matos, Los Ayalas), New York City (LP21), and Chicago's Humboldt Park (Evaristo "Tito" Rodriguez), and master vocalists trained in concert choral (William White), jazz (Mila Llauger), and Afro-Latin and Hip-hop lyricism. Since 2009, Isa has served as CEO for her independent label SotaRico, distributing over thirteen of her projects bridging her music mix and upbringing of Minnesota and Puerto Rican culture into a fusion of sound. She is known as one of the top artists in the Twin Cities, has been featured in every major publication in the state of Minnesota, and has performed nationally and internationally with her original music.

ABOUT THE ILLUSTRATOR

Kprecia is the owner and founder of Kp Inspires, a company created to push good energy into the world through the power of illustration. She uses art as a way to support businesses, create and sell unique product designs, and inspire. Kprecia's hope is to be an example to others like her to build their own door to walk through and remain authentic. Find her at @kpinspires on Instagram and at www.kpinspires.com.

ABOUT 826 MSP

826 MSP is a nonprofit youth writing center that empowers underserved Twin Cities students in grades K–12 to think creatively, write effectively, and succeed academically alongside a community of caring volunteers. The organization was founded in 2009 in response to Minnesota's opportunity gap, and continues to work toward ending inequities by amplifying student voice. Our youth writing center, located in South Minneapolis, provides a safe, welcoming creative space with a whimsical "oceanographic" theme. We sincerely believe that a fun, beautiful space helps to inspire, cultivate, and broadcast students' creativity.

In 2019, 826 MSP became the ninth and newest chapter of 826 National, a network of youth writing and tutoring centers in major cities throughout the United States. 826 National's philosophy is that individualized attention is critical to improving literacy and equipping students for success. We work toward our mission and serve our community through the following programs:

After-School Writing Lab: This program serves about fifty students, K–12, per semester. Hosting four days a week, we pair volunteer tutors one-on-one with students to offer academic support across all subjects.

Storytelling and Bookmaking Field Trips: Available to second- to fifth-grade classes across the Twin Cities, our field trips strive to embolden our next generation of writers to explore and value their own voice. Students and teachers join us to craft original narratives as a class. Volunteers, including an illustrator, work with student authors to publish a book within two hours.

Writers' Room: 826 MSP works in concert with the staff and students at South High School to create a drop-in satellite writing center within the school to support students and teachers for all their writing needs. For teachers this includes lesson plan support and project ideas, and for students this includes help with college essay writing, homework assignments, and even personal writing projects.

Creative Writing Workshops: Held periodically for a variety of ages and interests, each workshop represents a collaboration between student authors, volunteers, and community partners working to create original pieces around a theme.

Young Authors' Book Project: Classroom teachers, volunteers, and 826 MSP staff work together to support students in the creative process of writing original works around a theme. Illustrators, designers, publishers, and printers collaborate with students to create a professionally published anthology of their work.

Young Authors' Council: 826 MSP's newest youth leadership program connects youth through writing and civic engagement. Each school year, the program offers ten youth a paid fellowship, publishing opportunities, and leadership experience. YAC is open to students in grades six through twelve who attend Minneapolis or St. Paul schools.

LAND ACKNOWLEDGMENT

Today, seven Ojibwe reservations and four Dakota communities are located within the state of Minnesota—the place 826 MSP calls home. 826 MSP pays tribute to the Dakota and Ojibwe as the original people of this sacred land, first called Mni Sota Makoce in the Dakota language.

Mni Sota Makoce is a place that carries a deep, layered history across the thousands of years the Dakota and Ojibwe peoples have been in kinship with the land, and, in the centuries since, European settlers colonized the land that the state of Minnesota now occupies. The land seizures and genocide commited by the United States were projects of spiritual and cultural destruction that denied the Dakota free and unhindered access to the land that fundamentally shapes their identity. We acknowledge that trauma has occurred, that harm continues to occur today, and that it is incumbent upon all of us residing on this land to work toward an equitable future where everyone has the opportunity to thrive. We encourage you, too, to learn and consider the history of the land on which you reside, as well as the resilient peoples and complex legacies that have made it what it is today.